DISNEY's
WORLD of ENGLISH

BASIC ABC'S +

Book 2

Editor in Chief
Anne R. Dow
Harvard University

Author
Diane Warshawsky, Ph.D.

Consultant on Educational Philosophy
Shinichi Suzuki

2

3

Huey, Dewey, and Louie
look the same.

Tweedledee
and Tweedledum
look the same.

These cats look the same.

But these cats don't look the same.

These dogs all look the same.

But these dogs don't look the same.

5

1

Yes ■ ■ No

2

Yes ■ ■ No

3

Yes ■ ■ No

4

Yes ■ ■ No

Listen!
What are Huey, Dewey, and Louie doing?

They're blowing up balloons!

Huey takes a red balloon.

He starts to blow.

11

He blows…

and he blows…

and he blows!

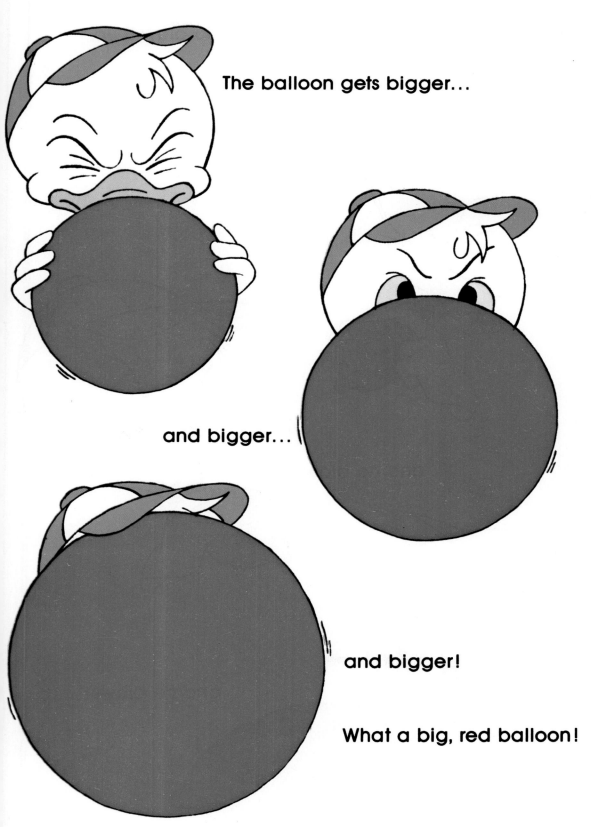

The balloon gets bigger...

and bigger...

and bigger!

What a big, red balloon!

Dewey takes a green balloon and starts to blow it up.

He blows…

and he blows…

and he blows!

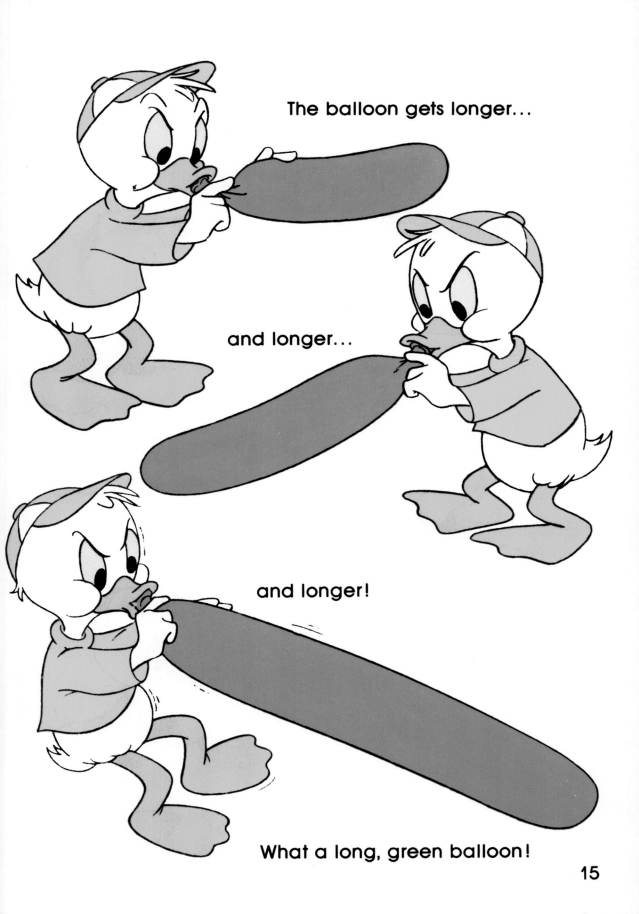

The balloon gets longer...

and longer...

and longer!

What a long, green balloon!

Louie starts to blow up a blue balloon.

He blows...

and he blows...

and he blows and he blows...

and he blows some more!

The balloon grows...

and grows...

and grows...

and grows until...

...until the balloon is bigger than Louie is,
or than Huey is,
or than Dewey is!

What a very, very, very big balloon!

Which balloon is Huey's?
Which balloon is Dewey's?
Which balloon is Louie's?

What color is Mickey's balloon?
What color is Minnie's balloon?

What color is the bed?
What color is the bean?
What color is the shoe?

Goofy is sleeping in a red bed.

Clarabelle is eating green beans.

Daisy is wearing blue shoes.

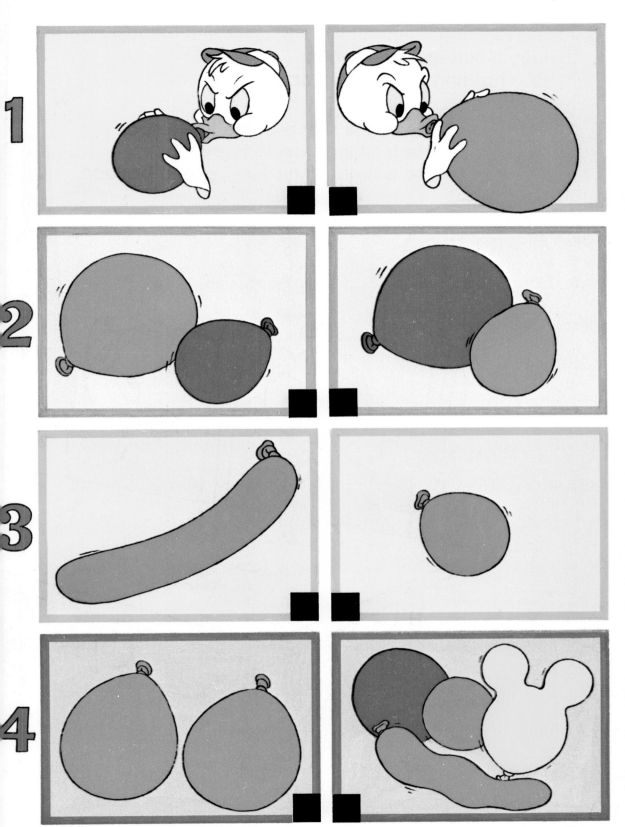

Huey is sitting at the table.
He is holding his big, red balloon.

Dewey is sitting at the table, too.
He is sitting next to Huey.
He is holding his long, green balloon.

Louie is sitting on his very, very big, blue balloon.
Louie's balloon is next to the table.

Look!
Where?
On the back of Huey's chair.
It's Chip!
He's holding a pin.
Uh oh!

Look!
Where?
Under the table.
It's Dale!
Uh oh!
He's holding a pin, too!

Look!
Where?
Over there!

On the chair!

On the back of the chair!

Behind the chair!

Next to the chair!

Under the chair!

In the air!

At the top of the stairs!

1

2

3

4

Chip sticks his pin in Huey's balloon.
The balloon breaks.

He sticks his pin in Dewey's balloon.
The balloon breaks.

Dale sticks his pin in Louie's balloon.
The balloon breaks...

and Louie falls!

Huey, Dewey, and Louie
see Chip and Dale.

Huey, Dewey, and Louie are very, very angry.

Chip and Dale start to run.

Huey, Dewey, and Louie
start to run after Chip and Dale.

Chip and Dale run around the room.

Huey, Dewey, and Louie run after them.

Chip and Dale run up the stairs.

Huey, Dewey, and Louie run after them.

Chip and Dale run down the stairs.

Huey, Dewey, and Louie run after them.

Chip and Dale jump
out the window.

Huey, Dewey, and Louie jump
out the window, too.

Chip and Dale run up a tree.

Huey, Dewey, and Louie
don't run up the tree.

They go back into the house...

and start blowing up balloons again.

Mickey says:

Clap your hands!

Turn around!

Put your hands up
in the air!

Bend down to the ground!

Touch your head!

Touch your toes!

Stand up straight!

Touch your nose!

Jump up and down!

Birthdays are fun —

Cake and ice cream—candles, too.
Birthday hats for me and you.
Gifts, balloons, and games to play,
A birthday is a very happy day!

1

2

3

4

Look! It's Mickey Magician!
He's doing another
magic trick.

He waves his magic wand,
and out comes...

...a cat
and another cat
and another cat!

Cats and cats and more cats!

Mickey puts some more magic letters in his hat.

Here, Daisy.

Thank you, Mickey.

FLOWER

Here, Minnie.

Oh, thank you, Mickey!

Mickey puts the letter **S** in his hat.

47

duck

ducks

chicken

cow

cows

48

dog

dogs

chickens

horse

horses

49

1 birthday cake

2 roses

3 gifts

10 happy faces

9 pieces of cake

8 ice cream cones

4 ribbons

5 candles

6 hats

7 balloons

Goodbye! See you at Pluto's birthday party!

SING ALONG!

Huey, Dewey, and Louie

My name is Huey.
My name is Dewey.
And Louie is my name.
I don't know which one is which,
'Cause they all look the same.
Huey looks like Dewey.
And Dewey looks like Louie.
My name is Huey.
My name is Dewey.
And Louie is my name.
And we all look the same.
And they all look the same.

Huey Takes a Red Balloon

Huey takes a red balloon,
And he starts to blow.
And as he blows that red balloon,
Well, it starts to grow.
He blows and blows and blows
  and blows.
The balloon just grows and grows
  and grows.
Oh, what a beautiful red balloon!
Oh, what a beautiful red balloon!

Dewey takes a green balloon,
And he starts to blow.
And as he blows that green balloon,
Well, it starts to grow.

He blows and blows and blows
  and blows.
The balloon just grows and grows
  and grows.
Oh, what a beautiful green balloon!
Oh, what a beautiful green balloon!

Louie takes a blue balloon,
And he starts to blow.
And as he blows that blue balloon,
Well, it starts to grow.
He blows and blows and blows
  and blows.
The balloon just grows and grows
  and grows.

Oh, what a very, very, very,
  very, very, very,
Oh, what a very big blue balloon!

Goofy Is Sleeping in a Red Bed

Goofy is sleeping in a red bed,
In a red bed, in a red bed.
Goofy is sleeping in a red bed.
Goofy's bed is red.
Not yellow,
Not blue,
Not green,
But red!
Goofy is sleeping in a red bed.
Goofy's bed is red.

Clarabelle's eating green beans,
Green beans, green beans.
Clarabelle's eating green beans.
Clarabelle's beans are green.

Daisy is wearing blue shoes,
Blue shoes, blue shoes.
Daisy is wearing blue shoes.
Daisy's shoes are blue.

Huey Is Sitting at the Table

Huey is sitting at the table,
At the table, at the table.
Huey is sitting at the table,
Holding his balloon.

Dewey is sitting at the table,
At the table, at the table.
Dewey is sitting at the table,
Holding his balloon.

Huey and Dewey are at the table,
At the table, at the table.
Huey and Dewey are at the table,
Holding their balloons.

We are sitting at the table,
At the table, at the table.
We are sitting at the table,
Holding our balloons.

Is Louie sitting at the table,
At the table, at the table?
Is Louie sitting at the table,
Holding his balloon?

No! Louie's not sitting at the table,
At the table, at the table.
Louie's not sitting at the table,
Holding his balloon.
He's sitting on his balloon!
He's sitting on his balloon!

Look! Where? Over There!

Look! Where? Over there!
On the chair! It's Chip and Dale!

Look! Where? Over there!
On the back of the chair!
  It's Chip and Dale!
Over where?
On the back of the chair,
On the chair,
It's Chip and Dale!

       on the chair
       on the back of the chair
       behind the chair
       next to the chair
       under the chair
       in the air
       at the top of the stairs

Around and Around

Around and around and
  around the room,
Around and around and
  around the room,
Around and around and
  around the room,
Around they go!

(Faster, faster, faster, faster!)

Up, Down

Up, down, up, down,
Down, up, down, up.
Up, up, up, up to the top!
Down, down, down, down,
  never stop!
Up the stairs they run, run, run!
Down the stairs they come,
  come, come!

Clap Your Hands!

1, 2, 3, 4,
1, 2, 3, 4,
Clap your hands now -
Clap, clap, clap!
Turn yourself around!
Put your hands up in the air!
Bend down to the ground!
Touch your head and touch
   your toes!
Stand up straight and touch
   your nose!

Clap your hands now —
Clap, clap, clap!
Now jump up and down,
And turn yourself around!
Turn yourself around!

Pluto's Birthday Song

Pluto's birthday is today.
Happy Birthday, Pluto!
H-A-P-P-Y, H-A-P-P-Y,
H-A-P-P-Y,
Happy Birthday, Pluto!
(clap) APPY
(clap, clap) PPY
(clap, clap, clap) PY
(clap, clap, clap, clap) Y
(clap, clap, clap, clap, clap)

Birthday, Birthday

Birthday, birthday, oh, what fun!
For you, for me, for everyone!
Birthday, birthday, all come along.
Join us and sing a little birthday song.
Cake and ice cream — candles, too.
Birthday hats for me and you.
Gifts, balloons, and games to play,
A birthday is a very happy day!

What Does a Duck Say?

What does a **duck** say?
(**Duck** say, **duck** say)
What does a **duck** say?
Does it say this:
Arf! Arf! Arf!
No, it doesn't!
Neigh!
No, it doesn't!
Moo!
No, it doesn't!
Cluck! Cluck! Cluck!
No, it doesn't!
Quack! Quack! Quack!
Yes, it does!
That's what a **duck** says!
(**Duck** says, **duck** says)
That's what a **duck** says!
Quack! Quack! Quack!

Duck - Quack! Quack! Quack!
Dog - Arf! Arf! Arf!
Chicken - Cluck! Cluck! Cluck!
Cow - Moo!
Horse - Neigh!

Let's Have a Birthday Party

Let's have a birthday party,
Birthday party, birthday party,
Let's have a birthday party
With a birthday cake!

How many **cakes** will there be,
Will there be, will there be?
How many cakes will there be,
One big birthday cake!

1 big birthday cake
2 roses on the cake
3 gifts to open
4 ribbons on the gifts
5 candles on the cake
6 birthday hats to wear
7 big balloons to pop
8 ice cream cones to lick
9 pieces of cake to eat
10 happy faces

Ten Little Candles

There is one, there are two,
There are three little **candles**,
There are four, there are five,
There are six little **candles**,
There are seven, there are eight,
There are nine little **candles**,
Ten little candles on the cake.

There was one, there were two,
There were three little pieces,
There were four, there were five,
There were six little pieces,
There were seven, there were eight,
There were nine little pieces,
Ten little pieces of that cake.

10 little candles on the cake
10 little pieces of that cake
10 hungry children eating cake

Notas

Notas